Piano Exam Pieces

ABRSM Grade 4

Selected from the 2015 & 2016 syllabus

Name

Date of exam

Contents

Editor for ABRSM: Richard Jones

First published in 2014 by ABRSM (Publishing) Ltd, a wholly owned subsidiary of ABRSM, 24 Portland Place, London W1B 1LU, United Kingdom © 2014 by The Associated Board of the Royal Schools of Music

Music origination by Julia Bovee
Cover by Kate Benjamin & Andy Potts
Printed in England by Halstan & Co. Ltd, Amersham, Bucks.

MIX
Paper from responsible sources
www.fsc.org FSC™ C109619

Tempo di Menuetto

No. 3 from *Six pièces très faciles*, Op. 52

J. N. Hummel
(1778–1837)

Six pièces très faciles Six Very Easy Pieces

The Austrian pianist and composer Johann Nepomuk Hummel was a child prodigy who studied with Mozart till the age of 10. Between the ages of 11 and 14 he toured northern Europe under his father's guidance, meeting Haydn in London. On his return to Vienna, he studied with Haydn, Albrechtsberger and Salieri. He held the posts of concertmaster to Prince Esterházy (Haydn's employer) at Eisenstadt (1804–11), and court Kapellmeister (music director) at Stuttgart (1816–18) and Weimar (from 1819). He also toured regularly as a virtuoso pianist, frequently performing his own music, from which he gained an international reputation.

Hummel's *Six pièces très faciles*, Op. 52, from which this Tempo di Menuetto is selected, were composed in 1811–12. They show Hummel still writing in the style of Haydn and Mozart, despite the huge stylistic advances since made by Beethoven. The formula 'Tempo di…', often used by European composers since the time of Corelli, denotes a composition that preserves the metre of the dance named but is otherwise only loosely related to it. A few slurs have been added by analogy with those of the original edition, and the dynamics have been added at the opening and in b. 32, and have been supplemented in the Trio.

Source: *Six pièces très faciles*, Op. 52 (Vienna: Artaria, 1815)

Adapted from Hummel: *16 Short Pieces*, edited by Timothy Roberts (ABRSM)

Tempo di Menuetto

CODA

A:2

La lutine

J. P. Kirnberger
(1721–83)

La lutine The Mischievous Sprite

Johann Philipp Kirnberger studied with Bach in Leipzig from 1739 to 1741. He then worked for various members of the nobility in Poland for 10 years (1741–51) before returning to Germany, where, from 1758 till his death, he worked in Berlin as court musician to Princess Anna Amalia of Prussia, sister of Frederick the Great. Among the most prominent Berlin theorists of the time, he promoted Bach's methods of composition in several important treatises. Kirnberger's own compositions are partly modelled on Bach's and partly on the more 'modern', *galant* style of Bach's sons. Kirnberger advocated the study of keyboard dances to help students develop a good sense of time and rhythm.

La lutine is freely written in dance style, but adopts the French custom of attaching a fanciful title to the piece as a clue to its expressive character. Kirnberger might well have been inspired by François Couperin's piece with the same title (from his first book of *Pièces de clavecin*, 1713), which was described by Wilfrid Mellers as 'a little piece about sprites and goblins such as were rampant in bacchanalian revels in masques and divertissements'. All slurs and dynamics are editorial suggestions only. **In the exam, the first repeat should be played**.

Source: F. W. Marpurg (ed.): *Clavierstücke mit einem practischen Unterricht für Anfänger und Geübtere, Dritte Sammlung* (Berlin: Haude & Spener, 1763)

Bourrée

Third movement from Partita in G minor

G. H. Stölzel
(1690–1749)

The German composer Gottfried Heinrich Stölzel studied at the University of Leipzig. After a tour of Italy (1713–15), he became Kapellmeister (music director) at the court of Gera (by 1718) and then at that of Saxe-Gotha (1719), where he remained for the rest of his life. Bach clearly had a high regard for Stölzel's music: he had a Passion-oratorio by Stölzel and two of his cantata cycles for the entire church year performed in Leipzig during the 1730s. Stölzel's aria 'Bist du bei mir', formerly attributed to Bach, was familiar to the Bach household; his Partita in G minor, from which this Bourrée is selected, was used by Bach for the musical education of his eldest son Wilhelm Friedemann.

The bourrée is a moderately fast French dance in duple time, popular in Baroque music from the time of Lully onwards. All slurs, staccatos and dynamics are editorial suggestions only. W. F. Bach clearly miscopied bb. 11–12, and they have been reconstructed here by the editor.
Source: *Clavier-Büchlein vor Wilhelm Friedemann Bach* (MS in the hand of J. S. and W. F. Bach, Cöthen, from 1720), New Haven, Conn., Yale University, Library of the School of Music

© 1988 by The Associated Board of the Royal Schools of Music
Adapted from J. S. Bach et al.: *A Little Keyboard Book*, edited by Richard Jones (ABRSM)

AB 3733

B:1

Canción para dormir una muñeca

No. 7 from *17 piezas infantiles*

Antonio Estévez
(1916–88)

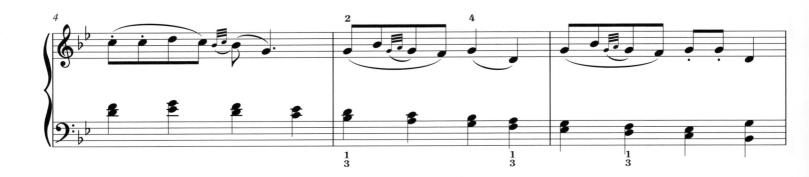

Canción para dormir una muñeca Lullaby for a Doll; **17 piezas infantiles** 17 Children's Pieces

Antonio Estévez was a Venezuelan composer, conductor and oboist. From 1934 to 1944 he studied oboe and composition at the School of Music and Declamation in Caracas, and played the oboe in the Venezuela Symphony Orchestra. During the Second World War, he also taught at the National School of Music in Caracas. After the war, he studied with Bernstein, Koussevitzky and others at Columbia University and Tanglewood. Estévez's earlier music was nationalistic in style, inspired by Venezuelan music and culture. From 1961 he adopted new orchestral and electroacoustic techniques, after studying electronic music in Paris. He also worked closely with kinetic painters Jesús Soto and Carlos Cruz Diez, and created multimedia works, including a 'sonic space' for the Jesús Soto Museum in Venezuela.

'Canción para dormir una muñeca' is one of *17 piezas infantiles* for piano. These pieces are so called because they take inspiration from Venezuelan children's activities and games.

poco meno mosso　　　　　**ancora più lento**

pp

rall.

p perdendosi sino al fine

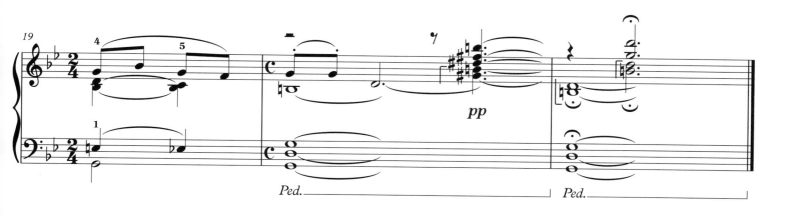

pp

Ped.

Ped.

B:2

Hej, znam ja łączkę

from *Ten nasz ogródeczek*, Op. 58

Feliks Rybicki
(1899–1978)

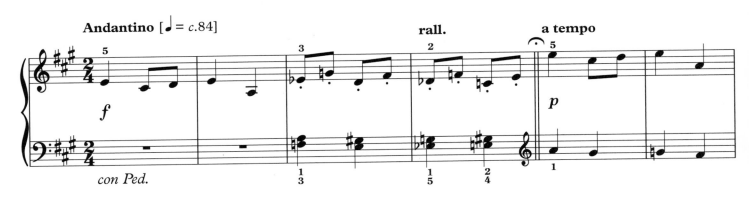

Hej, znam ja łączkę I Know of a Pleasant Meadow; **Ten nasz ogródeczek** This is Our Garden Fair

The Polish composer Feliks Rybicki studied composition and conducting at the Warsaw Conservatory in the early 1920s. Later, he conducted the Warsaw Philharmonic Orchestra, and both wrote and directed music for the Warsaw theatres and for Polish Radio. His output includes orchestral, vocal, chamber and piano music. Among the latter is his *Ten nasz ogródeczek*, Op. 58, a collection of 18 piano arrangements of Czech and Slovak folksongs (published in 1971), from which this piece is selected.

The main body of the piece consists of two different arrangements of the folksong 'Hej, znam ja łączkę' (bb. 5–20 and 21–36). These are framed by a brief introduction and conclusion (bb. 1–4 and 37–44) which, having stated the first five notes of the folksong, like a clarion call, then exhibit the kind of chromatic harmony that is used to accompany it. The absence of staccatos in bb. 39–40 (cf. bb. 3–4) is presumably intentional and linked to the *diminuendo* at this point.

B:3

Jägerliedchen

No. 7 from *Album für die Jugend*, Op. 68

Robert Schumann
(1810–56)

Edited by Howard Ferguson

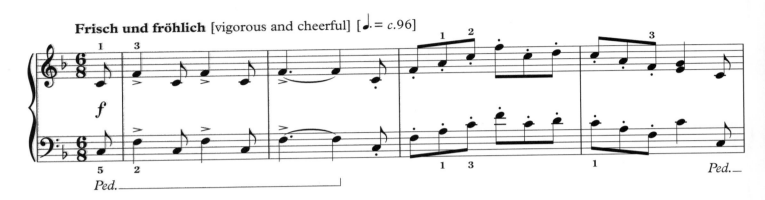

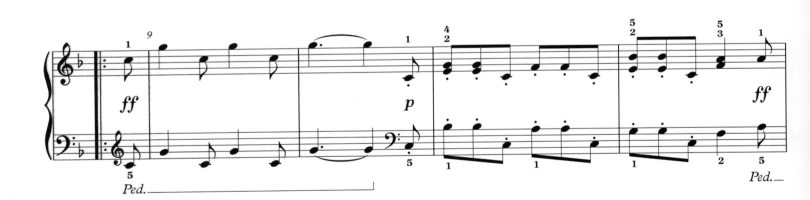

Jägerliedchen Huntsman's Song; **Album für die Jugend** Album for the Young

Robert Schumann's *Album for the Young*, Op. 68, from which this piece is selected, was composed in less than a month in 1848. At the time, the composer wrote: 'I don't remember ever having been in such good musical form…The pieces simply poured out, one after another.' Some of the 42 pieces in the collection, including 'Jägerliedchen', were dedicated to Schumann's daughter Marie on her seventh birthday.

In 'Jägerliedchen' we hear the call of the hunting horns (bb. 1–2 and 5–6), twice answered by a vigorous theme in staccato quavers. The two themes are combined in bb. 17–20. In the middle section (bb. 9–16), the *fortissimo* horn calls are answered by a new *piano* phrase in repeated notes. In this dialogue, one can imagine the headlong chase and the unlucky victim.

Source: *43* [*sic*] *Clavierstücke für die Jugend*, Op. 68 (Hamburg: Schuberth & Co., 1850)

Indian Pony Race

 C:1

D. C. Glover
(1925–88)

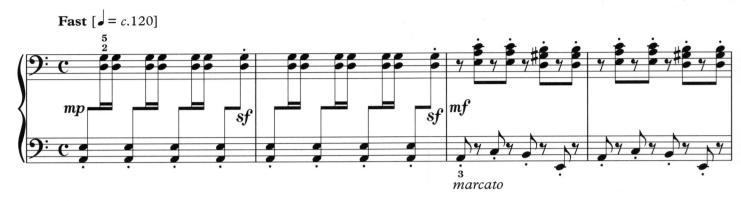

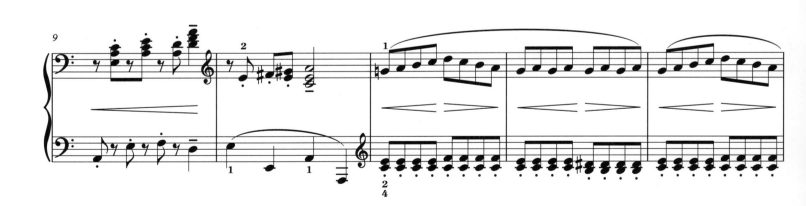

David Carr Glover was an American pianist, composer and music educator. Around 1944 he founded the Glover School of Music in Portsmouth, Virginia. From the early 1950s onwards he published a large number of original piano solos, specializing in books for piano students in varied styles, including boogie-woogie and jazz. He also wrote many piano courses and methods for students.

In the Shed

from *Piano Repertoire*, Level 2

Mike Cornick
(born 1947)

C:2

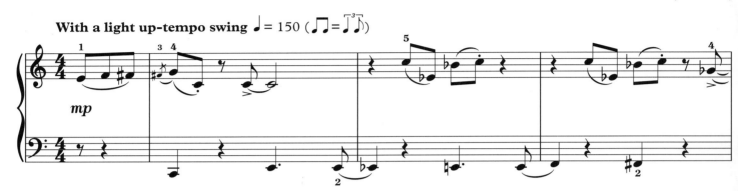

Mike Cornick studied composition at Trinity College of Music, London. He divides his time between school teaching, adult education, piano tuition and composition. His music is written in jazz and blues styles, and he has published many pieces of this type for educational purposes. Although the composer's metronome mark for 'In the Shed' is ♩ = 150, candidates may prefer a more moderate tempo, for example ♩ = *c*.130. Either tempo would be acceptable in the exam. **The repeat should be played in the exam.**

C:3

Progulka

No. 2 from *Musiques d'enfants*, Op. 65

Sergey Prokofiev
(1891–1953)

Progulka Promenade; **Musiques d'enfants** Music for Children

Sergey Prokofiev showed precocious talent in piano playing and composition from an early age. First taught by his mother – herself a pianist – he was writing his earliest piano pieces by the age of five. His mature output for the instrument is considerable, including nine sonatas and five concertos. In 1936, after 14 years' residence mainly in Paris, Prokofiev returned to his homeland, settling in Moscow. Music for children was highly regarded in the Soviet Union, and around the time of his return he wrote three children's compositions in close succession: *Musiques d'enfants*, Op. 65 (1935), *Peter and the Wolf*, Op. 67 (1936), and Three Songs for Children, Op. 68 (1936).

   Musiques d'enfants, from which 'Progulka' is selected, contains 12 pieces with programmatic titles, seven of which the composer arranged as a children's suite for small orchestra in 1941. 'Progulka' is a musical evocation of a stroll or outing. The right-hand parts in bb. 20–36 may be viewed as a dialogue between two walkers, as can the high and low (at first **mf** and **p**) left-hand parts in bb. 36–50. The indication *sempre p* in b. 24 is editorial.

Source: *Musiques d'enfants: douze pièces faciles*, Op. 65 (Berlin: Edition Russe de Musique, 1936)